Where is Little Bo Peep?

Celia Warren
Illustrated by Jill Newton

"Where is Little Bo Peep?"
said the wide-awake sheep.

“Where did she go?”

"I don't know," said the crow.

“Where can she be?
Did she hide up the tree?”

“No,” said the bee.
“She is not up the tree.”

"Did she hide in the boat?"

“No,” said the goat.
“She is not in the boat.”

“Where is Little Bo Peep?”
said the wide-awake sheep.
“Did she go in the house?”

"No," said the mouse.
"She is not in the house."

The wide-awake sheep looked for Little Bo Peep.

“I can’t find her,” he said.
He started to weep.

Then he went home,
all on his own,
wagging his tail behind him.

All the other sheep were
still asleep.

And there, in the middle, was Little Bo Peep!